Skills Builders

Spelling and Vocabulary

YEAR
3

Brenda Stones

RISING ★ STARS

PLEASE NOTE: THIS BOOK MAY NOT BE PHOTOCOPIED OR REPRODUCED AND WE APPRECIATE YOUR HELP IN PROTECTING OUR COPYRIGHT.

Rising Stars UK Ltd, 7 Hatchers Mews, Bermondsey Street, London SE1 3GS
www.risingstars-uk.com

Every effort has been made to trace copyright holders and obtain their permission for the use of copyright materials. The publishers will gladly receive information enabling them to rectify any error or omission in subsequent editions.

All facts are correct at time of going to press.

Published 2013
Reprinted with revisions 2014
Text, design and layout © 2013 Rising Stars UK Ltd

Project manager and editorial: Dawn Booth
Proofreader: Claire Shewbridge, Denise Moulton
Design: Words & Pictures Ltd, London
Cover design: Amina Dudhia
Acknowledgements: p.7 iStock/mightyisland; p.8 iStock/Igor Zakowski; p.10 iStock/Scott Wilson; p.12 iStock/Alias-Ching; p.14 Dave Thompson; p.20 iStock/otisabi; p.22 iStock/Kristijan Hranisavljevic; p.28 iStock/totallyjamie; p.30 iStock/Artisticco LLC; p.32 (top left) iStock/carduus; p.32 (middle left) iStock/djdarkflow; p.32 (middle right) iStock/mightyislan; p.32 (bottom left) iStock/imgendesign; p.32 (bottom right) iStock/Daniel Fisher; p.32 (bottom) iStock/Mark Stay; p.34 iStock/Logan Dance; p.36 iStock/Mark Stay; p.38 iStock/Kenn Wislander; p.40 iStock/Natural_Warp; p.42 *Oxford Junior Illustrated Dictionary*, Oxford University Press

British Library Cataloguing-in-Publication Data
A CIP record for this book is available from the British Library.

ISBN: 978-0-85769-699-1
Printed in Singapore by Craftprint International Limited

Skills Builders: Spelling and Vocabulary

YEAR 3

Contents

4   How to use this book

6   Revise plurals

8   Prefixes: pre-, re-

10   Prefixes: un-, in-, de-, dis-

12   Prefixes: super-, auto-, anti-

13   More prefixes: mis-, ex-, tele-, trans-

14   Root words: long and short vowel sounds

16   Revise suffix -ing, -ed (verbs)

18   Revise suffix -er, -est (adjectives)

20   Suffix -ous (adjectives)

22   Suffix -ly (adverbs)

24   Suffix -ture, -sure (nouns)

26   Suffix -tion, -sion (nouns)

28   Vocabulary: professions

30   Root words: word families

32   Apostrophes: revision

34   Apostrophes: possessive plural

36   Homophones

38   Common errors

40   Vocabulary: word origins

42   Using a dictionary

44   Vocabulary and Spellings

A1   Answers (centre pull-out)

How to use this book

The content and sequence of this series of Skills Builders on Spelling and Vocabulary are closely based on the revised National Curriculum for English.

Provided within this book:

1 Active teaching of individual spelling rules.

2 Emphasis on regular patterns in English spelling.

3 Writing grids to reinforce these spelling patterns.

4 Spelling jars and pots in which children make collections of common spellings.

5 Thematic vocabulary pages.

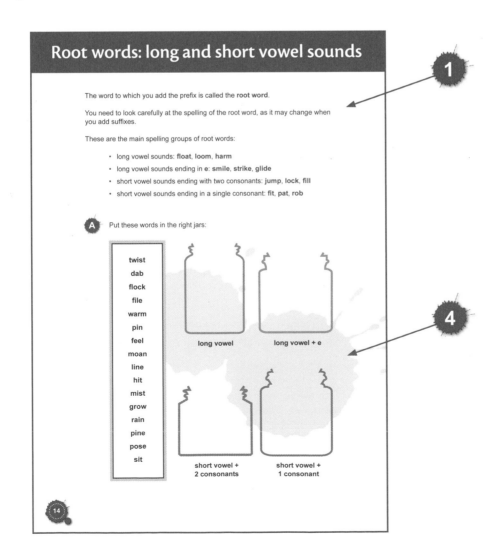

How to use this book

6   Occasional testing through dictation and word lists.

7   Two or three practical exercises for each section that progress in difficulty.

8   A variety of layouts, to help prepare for the GPS tests.

9   Encouragement of individual research in dictionaries and online.

10   Some more imaginative exercises on rhyme and alphabets.

11   'How did I do?' checks for self-evaluation.

12   Answers in a pull-out section for self-checking.

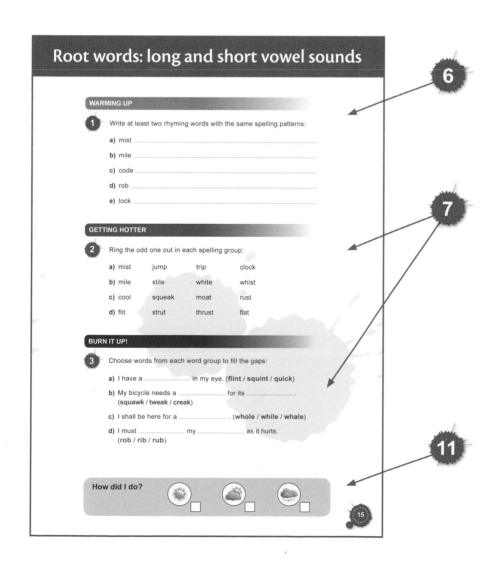

Root words: long and short vowel sounds

WARMING UP

1   Write at least two rhyming words with the same spelling patterns:

   a) mist _____

   b) mile _____

   c) code _____

   d) rob _____

   e) lock _____

GETTING HOTTER

2   Ring the odd one out in each spelling group:

   a) mist   jump   trip   clock

   b) mile   stile   white   whist

   c) cool   squeak   moat   rust

   d) flit   strut   thrust   flat

BURN IT UP!

3   Choose words from each word group to fill the gaps:

   a) I have a _____ in my eye. (**flint / squint / quick**)

   b) My bicycle needs a _____ for its _____ . (**squawk / tweak / creak**)

   c) I shall be here for a _____ . (**whole / while / whale**)

   d) I must _____ my _____ as it hurts. (**rob / rib / rub**)

How did I do? ☐ ☐ ☐

15

Revise plurals

Remember the rules for making plurals:

1 for most words, just add **s**: **bug**, **bugs**

2 for words that end **ss**, **sh**, **ch** or **x**, add **es**:
  box, **boxes**

3 for words that end in **o**, add **es**:
  tomato, **tomatoes**
  (but for words with a foreign origin just add **s**: **pianos**, **patios**)

4 for words that end in **y**, change to **ies**: **baby**, **babies**
  (but if there's a vowel before the **y**, just add **s**: **play**, **plays**)

5 for most words that end in a single **f** or **fe**, changes to **ves**: **knife**, **knives**

6 then there are irregular plurals, like **men**, **women**, **children**

 Write plurals for each rule:

i) table _____ book _____

ii) church _____ glass _____

iii) mango _____ cargo _____

iv) ferry _____ fly _____

v) half _____ dwarf _____

Revise plurals

WARMING UP

 1 Write plural animals for each rule:

a) beetle ⎯⎯⎯⎯⎯⎯⎯⎯⎯⎯⎯   zebra ⎯⎯⎯⎯⎯⎯⎯⎯⎯⎯⎯

b) fox ⎯⎯⎯⎯⎯⎯⎯⎯⎯⎯⎯   finch ⎯⎯⎯⎯⎯⎯⎯⎯⎯⎯⎯

c) flamingo ⎯⎯⎯⎯⎯⎯⎯⎯⎯⎯⎯   buffalo ⎯⎯⎯⎯⎯⎯⎯⎯⎯⎯⎯

d) wallaby ⎯⎯⎯⎯⎯⎯⎯⎯⎯⎯⎯   donkey ⎯⎯⎯⎯⎯⎯⎯⎯⎯⎯⎯

e) calf ⎯⎯⎯⎯⎯⎯⎯⎯⎯⎯⎯   wolf ⎯⎯⎯⎯⎯⎯⎯⎯⎯⎯⎯

f) mouse ⎯⎯⎯⎯⎯⎯⎯⎯⎯⎯⎯   sheep ⎯⎯⎯⎯⎯⎯⎯⎯⎯⎯⎯

GETTING HOTTER

2 Write plural foods for each rule:

a) carrot ⎯⎯⎯⎯⎯⎯⎯⎯⎯⎯⎯   apple ⎯⎯⎯⎯⎯⎯⎯⎯⎯⎯⎯

b) squash ⎯⎯⎯⎯⎯⎯⎯⎯⎯⎯⎯   Weetabix ⎯⎯⎯⎯⎯⎯⎯⎯⎯⎯⎯

c) potato ⎯⎯⎯⎯⎯⎯⎯⎯⎯⎯⎯   tomato ⎯⎯⎯⎯⎯⎯⎯⎯⎯⎯⎯

d) jelly ⎯⎯⎯⎯⎯⎯⎯⎯⎯⎯⎯   gravy ⎯⎯⎯⎯⎯⎯⎯⎯⎯⎯⎯

e) calf ⎯⎯⎯⎯⎯⎯⎯⎯⎯⎯⎯   salad leaf ⎯⎯⎯⎯⎯⎯⎯⎯⎯⎯⎯

BURN IT UP!

3 These plurals don't fit the rules. How many do you know?

a) woman ⎯⎯⎯⎯⎯⎯⎯⎯⎯⎯⎯   child ⎯⎯⎯⎯⎯⎯⎯⎯⎯⎯⎯

b) index ⎯⎯⎯⎯⎯⎯⎯⎯⎯⎯⎯   ibex ⎯⎯⎯⎯⎯⎯⎯⎯⎯⎯⎯

c) piano ⎯⎯⎯⎯⎯⎯⎯⎯⎯⎯⎯   radio ⎯⎯⎯⎯⎯⎯⎯⎯⎯⎯⎯

d) reef ⎯⎯⎯⎯⎯⎯⎯⎯⎯⎯⎯   clef ⎯⎯⎯⎯⎯⎯⎯⎯⎯⎯⎯

How did I do?   ☐   ☐   ☐

Prefixes: pre-, re-

Remember that a **prefix** goes **before** a word, and adds to its meaning.

> **Pre-** means **before**, as in **prepare**, **previous**, **predict**.
>
> **Re-** means **again**, as in **revisit**, **revise**, **restart**.

 A Match these words to their meanings:

predial	before historical time	redial	go back
prefabricate	dial a number in front	redo	dial a number again
predict	introduction to a book	return	make fresh again
preface	make beforehand	reappear	decorate again
prefix	say what will happen	redecorate	appear again
prehistoric	judge beforehand	refresh	start again
prejudge	before a word	restart	create again
prelims	pay beforehand	revise	call back
prelude	pages at the front of a book	recall	learn again
prepay	see before other people	recover	do again
preview	music at the beginning	recreate	get better again

Prefixes: pre-, re-

1 Choose the right words for the gaps:

revise   revamp   repair   retake   revisit

a) I must _____ my spellings for the test.

b) I can _____ the damage to my bicycle.

c) He will _____ the scene of the crime.

d) She must _____ her exams.

e) You should _____ the style of your room.

2 Choose the right words for the gaps:

predict   prehistoric   preorder   prefer   previous

a) We always _____ our dishes from the takeaway.

b) I can _____ what the weather will do.

c) Dinosaurs are _____ animals.

d) I _____ apples to pears.

e) The opening was _____ to the show.

3 Write your own sentences including these words:

a) prepare _____

b) presume _____

c) predate _____

d) repair _____

e) resume _____

f) relate _____

How did I do?

These prefixes all mean **not**:

> **un**able, not able; **un**tidy, not tidy
>
> **in**capable, not capable; **in**credible, cannot be believed
>
> **de**code, undo the code; **de**camp, leave the camp
>
> **dis**like, not to like; **dis**please, not to please

With the prefixes **un-**, **de-**, **dis-**, the spelling of the root word does not usually change. But with the prefix **in-**, the spelling changes before some consonants:

Prefix	Before	Becomes	Sample words
in-	i	ill	illegal
in-	m	imm	immature
in-	r	irr	irregular
in-	p	imp	imperfect

 A Using the prefix **in-**, write the words for:

> **a)** not distinct _____
>
> **b)** not legible _____
>
> **c)** not modest _____
>
> **d)** not relevant _____
>
> **e)** not possible _____

Prefixes: un-, in-, de-, dis-

1 Choose the right prefixes to make these words mean "not":

a) frost ....

b) lucky ....

c) obey ....

d) popular ....

e) compose ....

GETTING HOTTER

2 What do these words mean?

a) unusual ....

b) infrequent ....

c) disown ....

d) disappear ....

e) destabilise ....

BURN IT UP!

3 Look in your dictionary, and write more words for each of these prefixes:

a) un ....

b) in ....

c) de ....

d) dis ....

How did I do?

11

Prefixes: super-, auto-, anti-

super- means above, as in **superhero**

auto- means self, as in **autobiography**

anti- means against, as in **anti-clockwise**

 A   Add **super-**, **auto-** or **anti-** to the following words and sort them into the correct jar:

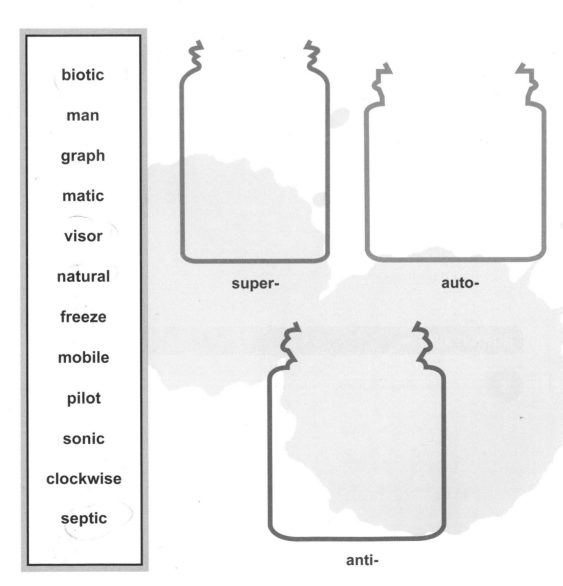

biotic

man

graph

matic

visor

natural

freeze

mobile

pilot

sonic

clockwise

septic

super-

auto-

anti-

More prefixes: mis-, ex-, tele-, trans-

> **mis-** means not, as in **misbehave**
>
> **ex-** means outside, as in **export**
>
> **tele-** means at a distance, as in **television**
>
> **trans-** means across, as in **transfer**

A   Add the prefix **mis-** to each of the following words to make a new word:

mis + behave =	misbehave
mis + lead =	
mis + adventure =	
mis + place =	
mis + fortune =	

B   Add the prefix **ex-** to each of the following words to make a new word:

ex + claim =	
ex + plode =	
ex + port =	

C   Add the prefix **tele-** to each of the following words to make a new word:

tele + phone =	
tele + vision =	
tele + graph =	
tele + port =	

D   Add the prefix **trans-** to each of the following words to make a new word:

trans + port =	
trans + fer =	
trans + parent =	
trans + mit =	

Root words: long and short vowel sounds

The word to which you add the prefix is called the **root word**.

You need to look carefully at the spelling of the root word, as it may change when you add suffixes.

These are the main spelling groups of root words:

- long vowel sounds: **float**, **loom**, **harm**
- long vowel sounds ending in **e**: **smile**, **strike**, **glide**
- short vowel sounds ending with two consonants: **jump**, **lock**, **fill**
- short vowel sounds ending in a single consonant: **fit**, **pat**, **rob**

 Put these words in the right jars:

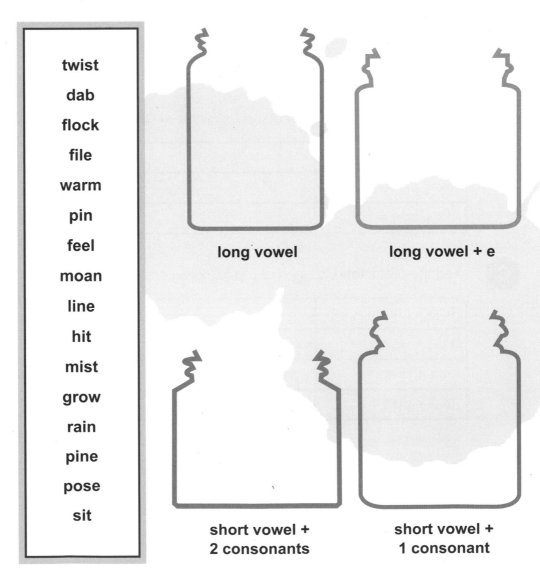

twist
dab
flock
file
warm
pin
feel
moan
line
hit
mist
grow
rain
pine
pose
sit

long vowel

long vowel + e

short vowel +
2 consonants

short vowel +
1 consonant

Root words: long and short vowel sounds

WARMING UP

 1 Write at least two rhyming words with the same spelling patterns:

a) mist ....

b) mile ....

c) code ....

d) rob ....

e) lock ....

GETTING HOTTER

 2 Ring the odd one out in each spelling group:

a) mist   jump   trip   clock

b) mile   stile   white   whist

c) cool   squeak   moat   rust

d) flit   strut   thrust   flat

BURN IT UP!

 3 Choose words from each word group to fill the gaps:

a) I have a .... in my eye. (**flint / squint / quick**)

b) My bicycle needs a .... for its ....
(**squawk / tweak / creak**)

c) I shall be here for a .... (**whole / while / whale**)

d) I must .... my .... as it hurts.
(**rob / rib / rub**)

How did I do? ☐ ☐ ☐

Revise suffix -ing, -ed (verbs)

Now we can add suffixes to verbs, which are "doing" words, like **jump** and **float**.

If we add the suffix **-ing**, we get **he is jumping** and **she was floating**.

If we add the suffix **-ed**, we get **he jumped** and **she floated**.

The spelling rules follow from the word groups we made in "Root words: long and short vowel sounds", page 14:

1. most words, just add **-ing** or **-ed**: **jump, jumping, jumped; float, floating, floated**

2. long vowel sounds ending in **e**, take off the **e**: **smile, smiling, smiled**

3. short vowel sounds ending in one consonant, double the last letter: **pat, patting, patted**

4. words ending in **y**: keep the **y** for **-ing**, change to **i** before **-ed**: **fry, frying, fried**

 List more words that follow each of these rules:

jump, jumping, jumped	smile, smiling, smiled	pat, patting, patted	fry, frying, fried

Revise suffix -ing, -ed (verbs)

 1 Write these parts of the verbs:

	-ing	-ed
start		
bake		
rely		
stun		
fit		
loan		
mate		

GETTING HOTTER

2 Fill the gaps with **-ed** words:

a) I (**try**) _____ to win but (**finish**) _____ last.

b) She (**start**) _____ well but (**rush**) _____ the corners.

c) He (**jump**) _____ the gun and (**fail**) _____ to qualify.

d) We (**hope**) _____ to win, but (**hop**) _____ to the finish.

BURN IT UP!

3 Fill the gaps with your choice of **-ing** words:

a) In the _____ race, I was _____ well when my friend began _____ .

b) We were _____ neck and neck, until he came _____ past me.

c) We were _____ towards the finish when he came _____ forward.

d) Finally, _____ back on the day, he was _____ all along.

How did I do?   ☐   ☐   ☐

17

Revise suffix -er, -est (adjectives)

You add the suffix **-er** and **-est** to adjectives, to make **comparative** forms.

	green		greener meaning more green		greenest meaning the most green

You don't need to change the spelling if:

- the short vowel sound is followed by two consonants, like **bold**, **bolder**, **boldest**
- there is a long vowel sound, so **mean**, **meaner**, **meanest**
- if the adjective ends in **e**, you don't double the **e**, so **white**, **whiter**, **whitest**

 Write these comparatives:

black	blacker	blackest
long		
short		
thick		
pale		
fine		

But if the adjective has a short vowel sound and ends with a single consonant, you double the last letter and add the ending, so **fat**, **fatter**, **fattest**.

And if the adjective ends in **y**, you change it to **i**, so **happy**, **happier**, **happiest**.

 Now write these comparatives:

fit	fitter	fittest
flat		
runny		
thin		
bony		
bonny		
slim		
trim		
grim		

Revise suffix -er, -est (adjectives)

WARMING UP

 1 Ring the odd one out, for each spelling rule:

a) better, fatter, later, hotter, flatter

b) thickest, boldest, dampest, flattest

c) bittier, tinier, happier, tinnier

d) nicer, wiser, wetter, finer, later

e) thinnest, trimmest, coldest, fittest

GETTING HOTTER

2 Add suffixes to these adjectives:

kind	kinder	kindest
thick		
slimy		
wet		
hot		
silly		
nice		
white		

BURN IT UP!

3 Write **-er** and **-est** adjectives in the gaps:

a) Yesterday was chilly, today is .... , and tomorrow will be the ....

b) He is thin, she is .... , and he is the .... of all.

c) I am nice, he is .... , and she is the .... of all.

d) This pool is warm, that one is .... , and that one is the ....

e) This one is tall, that one is .... , but those ones are the ....

How did I do?

Suffix -ous (adjectives)

Some adjectives end with the suffix **-ous**.

 A Take these nouns and add **-ous**. If they end with silent **-e**, remove the **e** before adding **-ous**.

	-ous
mountain	mountainous
cavern	
poison	
danger	
fame	
nerve	
pore	

B If the root word ends in **-our**, it changes to **-or** before you add **-ous**:

	-ous
glamour	glamorous
humour	
vigour	
rigour	
vapour	
clamour	
odour	

C If the root word ends in **-y**, it changes to **-i** before you add **-ous**:

	-ous
vary	various
envy	
fury	
glory	
study	

Suffix -ous (adjectives)

WARMING UP

 1 Fill in the **-ous** adjectives in the yellow and white squares, then find another word reading down the yellow column:

full of poison											
full of odour											
full of fame											
full of vapour											
full of glory											
full of fury											
always studying											

The word is: ....

GETTING HOTTER

 2 Finish this rhyming poem:

I envy my friends, I feel e.. .

My fury increases, I'm f.. .

But when I get known I'll be f.. .

I'll have glamour, I'll be terribly g.. .

BURN IT UP!

3 Write single word meanings for these adjectives:

a) odorous ....

b) vaporous ....

c) humorous ....

d) vigorous ....

e) furious ....

How did I do?

Suffix -ly (adverbs)

To turn an adjective into an adverb, you add the suffix **-ly**:
quick, **quickly**; **stern**, **sternly**.

An **adjective** describes a noun, whereas an **adverb** describes a verb:

> **He ran quickly after the quick fox.**
>
> **He talked sternly to the sterner teacher.**

Usually, you don't have to change the spelling.

 A   Add **-ly** to these adjectives to make adverbs:

> **i)** cross ....   **ii)** blunt ....
>
> **iii)** nice ....   **iv)** grim ....
>
> **v)** cool ....   **vi)** normal ....

There are three exceptions:

* If the root word ends in **-le**, you drop the **e** to make it **-ly**:
  gentle, **gently**; **simple**, **simply**; **noble**, **nobly**

* If the root word ends in **y**, you change it to **i** and add **-ly**:
  happy, **happily**; **angry**, **angrily**; **funny**, **funnily**

* If the root word ends in **-ic**, you add **-ally**:
  basic, **basically**; **drastic**, **drastically**; **frantic**, **frantically**

B   Make these adjectives into adverbs; the spelling may have to change before **-ly**:

> **i)** humble ....   **ii)** formal ....
>
> **iii)** dramatic ....   **iv)** pretty ....
>
> **v)** nervous ....   **vi)** shifty ....

Suffix -ly (adverbs)

WARMING UP

1 Make adverbs ending in **-ly**, changing the spelling where needed:

hungry	hungrily	cautious	
necessary		famous	
feeble		mental	
tricky		mindful	

GETTING HOTTER

2 Add suffixes to change noun > adjective > adverb:

noun	adjective	adverb
hunger	hungry	hungrily
truth		
poison		
brass		
tin		
force		

BURN IT UP!

3 Choose adverbs to write in these sentences:

a) She came down the stairs _____ .

b) He walked out of the room _____ .

c) _____ , I ate my dinner.

d) _____ , I rode off on my bike.

e) She entered, _____ , before leaving again.

How did I do?

Suffix -ture, -sure (nouns)

There are many nouns that sound as if they end in **-er** but are actually spelt **-ure**.

 A   We've put some in groups of three. Memorise each group, cover them and write their spellings. Then check back.

measure treasure pleasure	
enclosure disclosure composure	
picture mixture pasture	
adventure departure furniture	

Suffix -ture, -sure (nouns)

1 Here are some more nouns ending in **-ure**:

a) an animal: cr...

b) being seized: s...

c) how high you stand: st...

d) arts and music: c...

e) false teeth: d...

f) a special part: f...

GETTING HOTTER

2 From the list on the opposite page, choose the word for:

a) tables and chairs ....

b) something you enjoy doing ....

c) going away ....

d) mixing up ....

e) field (two words) ....

BURN IT UP!

3 Write the meaning of these **-ure** words:

a) leisure ....

b) capture ....

c) lecture ....

d) moisture ....

e) posture ....

f) vulture ....

How did I do?

25

Suffix -tion, -sion (nouns)

There are lots of nouns that end with the sound **shun**. How do you spell it?

Here are just some of the answers. It can help to go back to the spelling of the root word.

Spelling	When	Examples	
-tion	The most common spelling, including **-ation, -ition, -ction**. Use when the root word ends in **-t** or **-te**.	action injection	
-sion	Use when the root word ends in **-d** or **-de**.	expansion extension	
-ssion	Use when the root word ends in **-ss** or **-mit**.	expression permission	
-shion	These are just exceptions! They tend to come from foreign words.	cushion fashion	

A Add these words to the correct box of examples:

> invention   discussion   inflation
>
>   confession   comprehension
>
> admission   television   exception
>
>   decision   division

Suffix -tion, -sion (nouns)

WARMING UP

1 These words can all have a suffix sounding like **shun**.
Fill in the correct spellings.

complete	completion
transit	
omit	
inflate	
confess	
admit	
direct	
confect	
remit	
confuse	

GETTING HOTTER

2 What are the root words of these?

permit	permission
	comprehension
	extension
	inflation
	injection
	admission
	transmission
	invention

BURN IT UP!

3 What are the meanings of these words?

a) exception ....

b) revision ....

c) comprehension ....

d) inflation ....

e) transition ....

How did I do?

 ☐   ☐   ☐

27

Vocabulary: professions

Here is another spelling of the suffix **shun**: **-cian**.

It is the suffix for root words that end in **-c** or **-cs**, and these are usually people's jobs, like **politician** and **physician**.

 A Fill the jar with words for jobs. There are clues around the edge to help you.

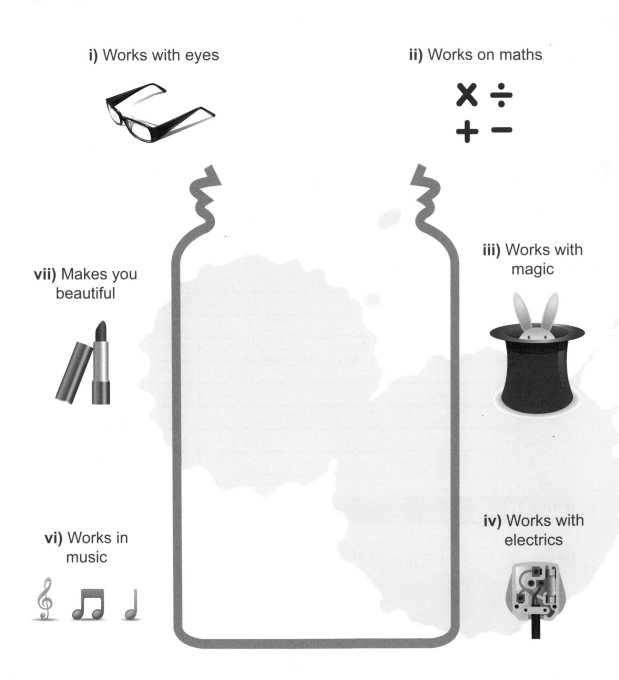

i) Works with eyes

ii) Works on maths

vii) Makes you beautiful

iii) Works with magic

vi) Works in music

iv) Works with electrics

v) Works with technology

Vocabulary: professions

1 Add more jobs, ending with **-er** and **-or**:

	-er
works on the land	
works with the law	
works in school	
does singing	
sells meat	
cuts men's hair	
sells bread	

	-or
works on the stage	
looks after health	
writes books	
edits books	
runs large towns	
sails at sea	
makes men's clothes	

GETTING HOTTER

2 Fill the gaps with any of the jobs on these two pages:

a) The job I'd most like to try is ....

b) The job I'd least like to try is ....

c) The job that would be the hardest is ....

d) The job that would be easiest is ....

BURN IT UP!

3 Fill the gaps with job words:

a) In a hospital you find .... and .... and
....

b) In a school you find .... and .... and
....

c) In the high street you find .... and .... and
....

How did I do? ☐ ☐ ☐

29

Root words: word families

What does **word family** mean?

A word family is a group of words built from the same root word. Word families may be built from prefixes and suffixes or from different word classes.

Word families can help you work out the spelling of the word by going back to the root word.

The **rest** word family:

rest

resting

restful

restroom

unrestful

A   Build your own word families using the following:

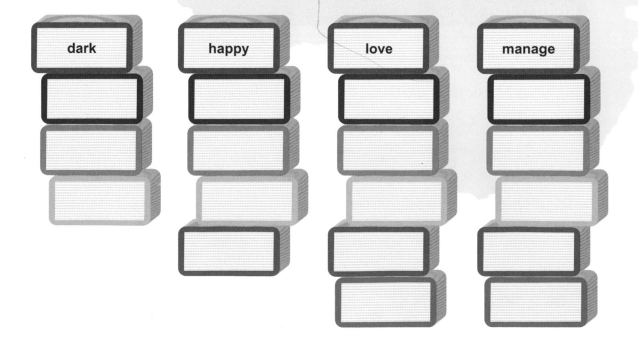

dark   happy   love   manage

Root words: word families

1 Build real words from these blocks:

	help	ful
un	stress	ness
dis	care	less
	hope	ing

....

....

....

Again, remember the spelling rules for adding suffixes.

GETTING HOTTER

2 Circle the odd one out in each of these word families:

a) prefer, refer, ferry, furry

b) provoke, revoke, vacation, provocation

c) parliament, parley, parsley, parlour

d) production, reduction, induction, education

BURN IT UP!

3 Choose the correct words to fill the gaps:

a) I have reached the top of my ....
   (**professor / professing / profession**)

b) I hope my cold will ....
   (**appear / reappear / disappear**)

c) We're expecting a visit from my ....
   (**relations / relating / related**)

d) This is the ice cream I .... (**prefer / refer / confer**)

e) This question is .... (**final / finished / finishing**)

How did I do?

 ☐   ☐   ☐

Apostrophes: revision

You have learned so far that there are two uses for the apostrophe:

- for missing letters, or contractions: e.g. **she'll**, **we've**, **it's**
- for possession, e.g. **the lady's shoes**, **the boy's helicopter**

 Match each sentence to one of these uses:

Where are my grandmother's socks?	
My grandmother's lost her socks.	
She's no idea where they are.	**contraction**
It's time we found them.	
My sister's socks are in the wash.	
They're blue and black.	
My grandmother's socks are blue.	
Blue's her favourite colour.	**possession**
They'll have to swap socks.	
Then everyone'll be happy.	

Please do not write in this book

Apostrophes: revision

 1 Write the root words or contracted forms to complete the table:

Root words	Contracted forms
I will	I'll
do not	
	I've
	can't
you are	

GETTING HOTTER

 2 Chose a contraction to complete each sentence:

a) The boy (**could'nt / don't**) do his homework.

b) I (**didn't / can't**) have enough time to play the game.

c) I (**won't / shouldn't**) be able to help you tomorrow.

d) You bought the present (**didn't / isn't**) you?

BURN IT UP!

3 Write four sentences which use an apostrophe for possession:

a) ....

....

b) ....

....

c) ....

....

d) ....

....

How did I do?   ☐   ☐   ☐

Apostrophes: possessive plural

So far we've only done possessives for single owners: the **dog's** bone, my **sister's** socks.

But if the owners are plural, the apostrophe goes after the **s**: two **dogs'** bones, my **sisters'** socks.

 A Rewrite these sentences making everything plural:

i) My sister's cup is blue.

Our sisters' cups are blue.

ii) What colour is her cup's handle?

iii) It's beyond his garden's fence.

iv) He's following the ship's funnel.

v) The baby's rattle is his favourite toy.

If the plural owners don't end in **s**, the apostrophe goes **after** the owners and before the **s**:

the **children's** shoes, the **men's** socks, the **sheep's** tails.

 B Write these as possessive phrases:

i) the tails of the mice

ii) the hair of the women

iii) the books of the children

iv) the shoes of the policemen

v) the sacks of the postwomen

Apostrophes: possessive plural

WARMING UP

1   Turn these into possessive phrases:

a) the shoes of the ladies

b) the shoes of the men

c) the mugs of the babies

d) the ears of the donkeys

e) the tails of the monkeys

f) the rings of the women

GETTING HOTTER

2   Rewrite these sentences in the plural:

a) Her baby's tooth fell out.

b) This man's shoe is worn out.

c) That woman's bag has fallen down.

d) The fox's tail is called a brush.

BURN IT UP!

3   Write sentences that include one contraction and one plural possessive:

a)

b)

c)

d)

e)

f)

How did I do?

Homophones

Homophones are words that sound the same but are spelt differently and have different meanings.

 A   Here is a list of homophones. Write their different meanings:

i) beach / beech ....

ii) blue / blew ....

iii) board / bored ....

iv) bread / bred ....

v) currant / current ....

vi) dear / deer ....

vii) flour / flower ....

viii) guessed / guest ....

ix) hair / hare ....

x) horse / hoarse ....

xi) key / quay ....

xii) lain / lane ....

xiii) loan / lone ....

xiv) made / maid ....

xv) missed / mist ....

xvi) moor / more ....

xvii) pale / pail ....

xviii) pane / pain ....

xix) pair / pear ....

xx) pause / paws ....

xxi) read / reed ....

xxii) right / write ....

xxiii) rows / rose ....

xxiv) seam / seem ....

xxv) tail / tale ....

Homophones

WARMING UP

1 Write homophones for these words:

a) banned _____ **b)** bawl _____ **c)** barred _____

d) fawn _____ **e)** lute _____ **f)** lessen _____

g) mare _____ **h)** maize _____ **i)** source _____

GETTING HOTTER

2 Choose the right spellings for these gaps:

a) In the _____ in the traffic, he pressed on the _____ . (**brake / break**)

b) It is only _____ that you pay the right _____ . (**fair / fare**)

c) If you give us some _____ , I'll give you a _____ of cake (**peace / piece**)

d) When we _____ up, let's have lunch of _____ and vegetables. (**meat / meet**)

e) He let out a _____ at how much her hair had _____ . (**groan / grown**)

f) She came in _____ so that she could _____ the music better. (**hear / here**)

g) _____ sure that _____ socks were hanging _____ . (**there / their / they're**)

h) _____ sitting on _____ tail. (**it's / its**)

i) I've _____ what happens behind the _____ . (**scene / seen**)

j) She _____ about which _____ she was on. (**sighed / side**)

k) _____ of the best minds have failed to solve that _____ . (**sum / some**)

l) Let's _____ at what is sitting on the _____ . (**stair / stare**) '

BURN IT UP!

3 Choose six homophones and write sentences that include both, as above:

a) _____

b) _____

c) _____

d) _____

e) _____

f) _____

How did I do?

 ☐   ☐   ☐

Common errors

Many common errors are homophones. But if you work out which word class you're trying to spell, it may make the spelling easier. Here are four examples.

It's / its

It's is a contraction of **it is** or **it was**.

Its is a possessive adjective, like **his** or **her**, which never has apostrophes.

So if you're not sure which is right, ask if it stands for **it is**, or whether you could substitute **his** or **her**.

 Complete the following:

> **i)** _____ sitting on _____ tail.
>
> **ii)** _____ perch is where _____ stuck.

They're / their

This is exactly the same rule:
They're is a contraction of **they are**; **their** is a possessive adjective.

B Complete the following:

> **i)** _____ sitting on _____ bench.
>
> **ii)** _____ bench is behind _____ garden.

Affect / effect

These sound slightly different and are different word classes.
Affect is a **verb**; **effect** is a **noun**.

C Complete the following:

> **i)** What is the _____ of this change?
>
> **ii)** Will it _____ us much?

Accept / except

Accept is a **verb**; **except** is a **preposition**, which comes before a noun.

 Complete the following:

> **i)** I'll _____ any drink _____ milk.
>
> **ii)** _____ for tea, I don't _____ hot drinks.

Common errors

WARMING UP

1 Link these words to their right word classes:

it's
accept
its
their
affect
they're
effect

verbs
nouns
adjectives

GETTING HOTTER

2 Complete these sentences with words from the boxes above:

a) _____ important how this will _____ us.

b) _____ not sure if they'll _____ the decision.

c) The _____ of _____ decision is vital.

d) I _____ that _____ not my decision.

BURN IT UP!

3 Write your own sentences with these pairs of words:

a) it's / its _____

b) their / they're _____

c) affect / effect _____

d) accept / except _____

How did I do?

 ☐   ☐   ☐

Vocabulary: word origins

Many English words have spellings and sounds that come from other languages.

Greek hard **ch-**: **school chemist**
Greek **-ph**: **graph phonics photo**
Latin **sc-**: **science scissors**
French soft **ch-**: **chef chalet**
French **-que**: **antique unique**
French **-gue**: **league tongue**

France
chef, chalet
antique, unique
league, tongue

Germany

Spain

Greece
school, chemist
graph, phonics,
photo

UK

GERMANY

FRANCE

SPAIN

ITALY

GREECE

Italy
science, scissors

Vocabulary: word origins

 1 Here are more words with these spellings.
Add them to the right countries of origin on the map opposite:

chorus	**mosque**	**brochure**
telephone	**champagne**	
character	**muscle**	**phoneme**

GETTING HOTTER

 2 There are other words that we use exactly as they are in European languages.

Add these words to the right countries on the map opposite:

pizza	**kindergarten**	**paella**
data	**café**	

BURN IT UP!

 3 Find out the meaning of these foreign words we use in English:

a) circa

b) interregnum

c) versus

d) déjà vu

e) al fresco

How did I do?

Using a dictionary

In a dictionary words are presented in alphabetical order so that we can find them easily. On this page all of the words begin with the letter **a**, so we need to look at the second or third letter in the word to find the order.

Running head

Alphabetical order

Headword

Numbered meanings

Definition

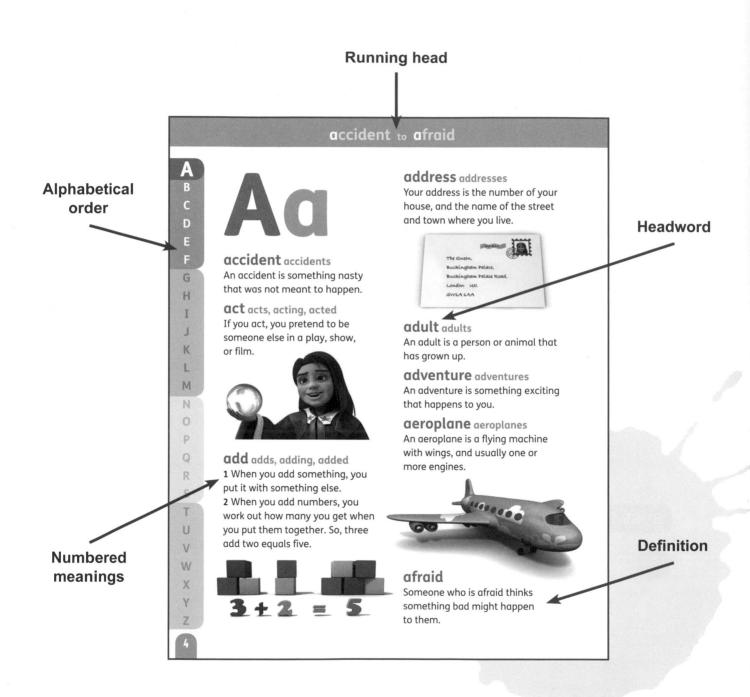

accident to afraid

Aa

accident accidents
An accident is something nasty that was not meant to happen.

act acts, acting, acted
If you act, you pretend to be someone else in a play, show, or film.

add adds, adding, added
1 When you add something, you put it with something else.
2 When you add numbers, you work out how many you get when you put them together. So, three add two equals five.

3 + 2 = 5

address addresses
Your address is the number of your house, and the name of the street and town where you live.

The Queen,
Buckingham Palace,
Buckingham Palace Road,
London UK
SW1A 1AA

adult adults
An adult is a person or animal that has grown up.

adventure adventures
An adventure is something exciting that happens to you.

aeroplane aeroplanes
An aeroplane is a flying machine with wings, and usually one or more engines.

afraid
Someone who is afraid thinks something bad might happen to them.

4

Using a dictionary

WARMING UP

 1 Put these words in the order they would appear in a dictionary:

a)

crucial	crouton	crossing	crossword	crowd

b)

persuade	pest	personality	persist	person

GETTING HOTTER

2 Use your dictionary to find the correct spelling of these words:

b _____ w _____ f _____ c _____ i _____

BURN IT UP!

3 Use these words in a sentence:

a) century

b) particular

c) reign

d) material

e) extreme

f) peculiar

How did I do?

Vocabulary and spellings

These are some of the words that you are expected to understand and spell in Year 3.

WARMING UP

 1 Practise writing and spelling the following words:

Word	Look	Cover	Say	Check
naughty				
promise				
various				
height				
different				
calendar				

GETTING HOTTER

 2 Underline the word that is spelt correctly:

reggylar	reguler	regular
experiment	experiment	experiement
scentre	centre	sentre
ordinary	ordinery	ordinnary
continu	contindue	continue
believ	beleive	believe
supose	sippose	suppose
remeber	rememmber	remember
spesial	special	speciall

BURN IT UP!

3 Use each word in a sentence:

a) certain

b) promise

c) knowledge

d) surprise

e) increase

f) decide

How did I do? ☐ ☐ ☐